Small Knight and George and the PIRATES

To Tomas, Kate and Samuel with love
R. A.

To Elias with oceans of love
A. R.

ORCHARD BOOKS
338 Euston Road, London NW1 3BH
Orchard Books Australia
Level 17/207 Kent Street, Sydney, NSW 2000

First published in 2012 by Orchard Books

Text © Ronda Armitage 2012
Illustrations © Arthur Robins 2012

A CIP catalogue record for this book is available from the British Library.

ISBN 978 1 40831 273 5

10 9 8 7 6 5 4 3 2 1
Printed in China

Orchard Books is a division of Hachette Children's Books,
an Hachette UK Company.
www.hachette.co.uk

Pirates

Small Knight and George and the PIRATES

Ronda Armitage Arthur Robins

ORCHARD

SMALL Knight and his friend George lived in an old castle on a high, spiky hill. Small Knight didn't mind that it was old but Mum and Dad Knight were worried.

Down in the courtyard,
Small Knight and George were
playing one of their favourite games,

'Pirates
Ahoy'.

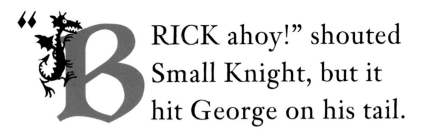"BRICK ahoy!" shouted Small Knight, but it hit George on his tail.

"OUCH!"

Yes, the old castle needed mending, but there was no money for the repairs.

"I've got it!
Pirates!"
exclaimed Dad Knight.
"Pirates and treasure!"
exclaimed Mum Knight.

"**S**MALL Knight, it's time for you to be a pirate," said Dad Knight.

"Here's your first crew . . .

. . . and your first pirate ship . . .

. . . and your first treasure map."

SMALL Knight's knees
knocked and his toes trembled.
He didn't want to go to sea
but he was worried about the castle
and he liked the bit about treasure.

The crew loaded provisions onto
the *Tiger Tim* and set sail.

"With our sails a-flap in the breeze
    We'll roam the seven seas
We'll do our very best
    To find a treasure chest
full of gold and jewell-er-y."

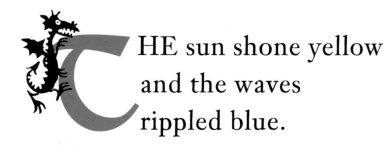 HE sun shone yellow and the waves rippled blue.

They came to Bare Rock. "Ahoy there, me hearty!" shouted Small Knight.

"I'm looking for treasure. Do you know which way to go?"

"Find Captain Swashmebuckle,"
said Small Kydd. "The biggest,
meanest pirate to sail the seven
seas but, wherever he is, that's
where the treasure will be.
If you rescue me,
I'll help you search."

"Welcome aboard,"
said Small Knight.

THE sun shone yellow and the waves rippled turquoise. George spied a pirate clinging to a raft. "Ahoy there, me hearty!" shouted Small Knight. "We're looking for Captain Swashmebuckle and the *Smelly Rose*. Have you seen them sailing by?"

"Don't talk to me about Captain Swashmebuckle," cried Small Bonny.

"The nastiest pirate to sail the seven seas. Threw me overboard. Are you sure you want to find the *Smelly Rose*?"

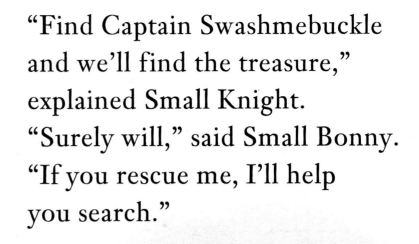

"Find Captain Swashmebuckle and we'll find the treasure," explained Small Knight. "Surely will," said Small Bonny. "If you rescue me, I'll help you search."

"Welcome aboard," said Small Knight.

THE clouds grew dark
and a great storm raged.
The *Tiger Tim* tossed
in the wallowing waves.
"Hold tight, me hearties!"
shouted Small Knight.

THE sun shone yellow and the waves flickered white. "Land ahoy," shouted Small Knight. "Ship ahoy, too. It's the *Smelly Rose* and it's sinking fast."

"Looky here, those be Captain Swashmebuckle's footprints," said Small Bonnie.

The pirates followed the enormous footprints along the silvery sand . . .

. . . over the
humpity hill . . .

. . . past the
prattling parrots . . .

. . . until they came to . . .

CAPTAIN SWASHMEBUCKLE!

He was **huge**!
OH, YES!

He was **fierce**!
OH, YES!

He was **mean**!
OH, YES!

SHE was crying.
Oh, no!

"My *Smelly Rose* is wrecked
and my treasure has gone.
Nobody loves me,
everybody hates me.
BOO HOO, BOO HOO!
What shall I do?"

"Please don't cry," said
Small Knight. "We'll help
you find your treasure."

"**W**HOOPEE! There she is, there's my treasure," shouted Captain Swashmebuckle.

"But that's a parrot!" exclaimed Small Knight.

"She's treasure to me," said Captain Swashmebuckle. "Coochie, coochie coo. Who's a pretty boy, then?"

SMALL Knight and his crew were dismayed. They explained why they needed gold and silver treasure.

"Don't worry, me young sprogs," said Captain Swashmebuckle. "I've got some of that, too." She opened the chest.

"I don't want to be nasty
and mean anymore. I'd like
to share the treasure with
some new friends, if I may?"

"Thank you," said Small Knight.
"And you can have a home
on the *Tiger Tim*."

THE pirates heaved the treasure chest over the humpity hill . . .

. . . and across the silvery sands to the *Tiger Tim*. Captain Swashmebuckle followed behind.

As the Tiger Tim set sail, the crew sang
their own sea shanty.

"With our sails a-flap in the breeze,
We've roamed two of the seas.
We've done our very best
We've found a treasure chest
full of gold and jewell-er-y."

Mum and Dad Knight were waiting on the drawbridge. "Hello, Mum," called Small Knight. "I've brought some new friends home." "How de do Ma'am," said Captain Swashmebuckle.

"BUT THEY'RE PIRATES!" whispered Mum Knight.

"VERY NICE pirates, with treasure!"

Mum and Dad Knight scrambled up to the Minstrels' Gallery.

"That's NOT treasure!"

they said.

"I'M a bit of a treasure, meself!" said Captain Swashmebuckle. "I loves swinging high. I'll mend this old castle for you."

Mum and Dad Knight were very
pleased with Captain Swashmebuckle.
"Do be careful, dear," they cried
as she dangled from the tower.

ut was Captain Swashmebuckle
always such a good pirate?
Of course not. She could still
be very nasty, mean and fierce
when the occasion arose.